"Face it and Feel it"

10 Simple (But Not Easy) Ways to Live Well With Anxiety

by Kimberly Morrow, LCSW

www.livingwellwithanxiety.com

Printed in the United States of America

ISBN 978-1-4507-9345-2

Cover Design and Editing: Melissa Gawlinski, Heaven-Sent Creative Concepts
"Face It and Feel It" and "Kimberly Joy Morrow" Logo Concepts by Kelly Craig

Anxiety quotes shared with permission from "Top 100 Inspirational Quotes for Living Anxiety-Free," compiled and edited by Deanne Repich, Director, National Institute of Anxiety and Stress, Inc., 900 E. Pecan St., Ste. 300-305, Pflugerville, TX 78660
www.conqueranxiety.com

Special thanks to:

Jeff and Francoise, my friends and colleagues, for encouraging me to go farther than I thought possible and to my husband and children for your unwavering support of my passion!

Contents

Intro

About Kimberly

What Is Anxiety?
Why Would My Brain Do This To Me?
How Do I Get Better?

10 Steps
1. Bring It On
2. Do the Opposite
3. Cognitive Therapy
4. The Role of Family
5. Safety Behaviors
6. Breathe
7. Be Mindful
8. Tap It Out
9. Exercise
10. Become Balanced

Final Thoughts

Resources

www.livingwellwithanxiety.com

About Kimberly Joy Morrow

Kimberly is a Licensed Clinical Social Worker and has been treating people with anxiety for more than 20 years and training professionals for more than 10 years. She has lived with anxiety her entire life and has found the skills she is going to share with you to be invaluable in her own journey with anxiety.

She is dedicated to helping people who suffer with anxiety; teaching professionals how to successfully treat anxiety disorders; and guiding people to a more fulfilling, balanced life.

Kimberly received a Masters Degree in Psychology from Memphis State University and a Masters Degree in Social Work from the University of Wisconsin-Milwaukee. She is on the Professional Education Committee of the Anxiety Disorders Association of America and the Scientific Advisory Board of the Obsessive Compulsive Foundation of Northwestern Pennsylvania.

www.livingwellwithanxiety.com

Kimberly is also a graduate of the Obsessive Compulsive Foundation's Behavior Therapy Institute and has had extensive training in Cognitive Behavioral Therapy, including Exposure and Response Prevention. Kimberly is dedicated to training others to treat anxiety, including providing workshops and supervision. She has developed a training video for the Anxiety Disorders Association of America to help emerging professionals become interested in treating anxiety. Also, she provides Wellness workshops to teach complementary ways to manage stress and anxiety in your life.

When you're feeling anxious, remember that you're still you. You are not anxiety. Whenever you feel otherwise, remember that's just the anxiety talking. You are still you and hold the power in every moment.

–Deanne Repich, *Top 100 Inspirational Quotes for Living Anxiety-Free*

Intro

This book is dedicated to all of those people who suffer with anxiety. I have been one of you. It can be a paralyzing force or just a real nag. Whichever it is for you, there are simple ways, when practiced consistently, which can help you live well with anxiety. I'd like to share the skills that have freed me from fear and that I have taught my clients and other professionals for over 20 years.

What Is Anxiety?

Anxiety is a normal reaction to stress. It can help one deal with a stressful situation at work, study for a test, or keep focused for a presentation. But when anxiety becomes an excessive, irrational experience that affects your personal or professional life, it has become an anxiety disorder.

Anxiety is one of the most debilitating and common disorders. Over 40 million people throughout the United States suffer with some form of anxiety. Of the $140 billion dollars that is spent on mental disorders, $42 billion is spent on anxiety disorders alone. There are varying degrees of anxiety that range from a few symptoms to extreme episodes that affect a person's functioning. There are also varying types of anxiety.

Generalized Anxiety Disorder (GAD)

GAD affects an estimated 6.8 million people and is characterized by constant tension, excessive worrying, and restlessness for long periods of time. These people can also experience physical symptoms due to the chronic nature of this condition. Typically, a person with GAD fears negative feelings, and so the worrying and tension is a coping strategy to try to protect them from future negative experiences.

Obsessive Compulsive Disorder (OCD)

Over 2.2 million people suffer from OCD which is one of the most physically and mentally draining forms of anxiety. A person with OCD will experience obsessions which are thoughts or images that create intense anxiety. They then engage in compulsions or behaviors to reduce this anxiety. Unfortunately, those compulsions only serve to give power to their fears and continue the cycle of OCD.

Panic Disorder

Panic Disorders are characterized by "panic attacks" which create a feeling of terror. Often people feel they are having a heart attack and present to the emergency room or their primary care physician due to their extreme physiological experience of panic. Common symptoms include: increased heart rate, chest pain, nausea, difficulty breathing, chills/hot flashes, fear of dying, and the feeling of not being in your body. Panic attacks often happen without warning which makes it difficult to prepare for them.

Social Phobia

Social phobia affects more than 15 million people. It is characterized by the fear of being judged by others or fear of being embarrassed in front of others. Often people with social phobia become isolated and lag behind in social skills because they do not participate in social experiences to help them gain these important skills. When forced to be in triggering situations, people often engage in safety behaviors to get them through the anxiety (hands in pockets, makeup to hide the blotches on their face, a drink to steady their hands, etc.)

Post Traumatic Stress Disorder (PTSD)

7.7 million people are affected by the symptoms of PTSD. This is generally brought on by a traumatic event in a person's life. It is characterized by intrusive memories, avoidance of triggers, and increased anxiety or emotional arousal.

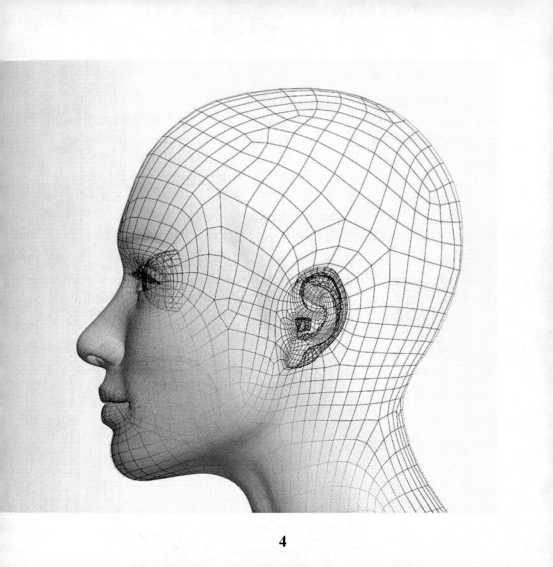

Why Does My Brain Do This To Me?

One thing I've learned about anxiety is that it can affect everyone: young or old, black or white, rich or poor. However, I find that everyone gets stuck on "why is this happening?" Anxiety happens for a variety of reasons but we know, for sure, that our brain is programmed to send us danger signals and we are programmed to listen to our brain. Unfortunately, some of us are born with this part of our brain sending out signals that are inaccurate. It can out-and-out lie to us by telling us something bad is going to happen when it actually is not (in the case of OCD), or it can exaggerate a danger to convince us to act on something that is actually quite insignificant (as in Panic). Sometimes it can get us to stay in our heads for hours on end just to ruminate about what might happen, convincing us that if we think about it long enough we will "figure it out," or at least avoid the impending bad feelings.

These danger signals trigger the release of a chemical called serotonin. When serotonin is out of balance, you feel anxious. It is your instinct to do something to feel better by avoiding the trigger, seeking out reassurance, or engaging in other behaviors that lessen the discomfort. However, every time you do this you are connecting the circuit in your brain, which will ensure that your brain will continue to send you these erroneous messages.

Dave Carbonell, Ph.D., an expert in the field of anxiety (www. anxietycoach.com) and founder of the Anxiety Treatment Center in Chicago, Illinois, describes another way to understand anxiety. He explains that when you are experiencing anxiety, you often are protecting yourself from a perceived danger, one that likely does not exist. It may feel like there is danger, but if you pay close attention, the truth is that it is only discomfort. Each time you engage in some kind of protective behavior, you give information to your brain that there really was a danger, therefore, more chemicals are released, you protect yourself again, and the cycle repeats and gets stronger.

Your brain can bully you by finding the areas in your life where you are most vulnerable and sending you fear or worries about these areas. For example, a young mother might fear harming her child; an electrician might worry he will cause a fire; or a gifted student might be concerned that he didn't study enough. People who know you realize that you are the opposite of your fear, but that does nothing to reassure you because you cannot stop worrying about the things that are most important to you.

People with anxiety can also find themselves ruminating about the regrets they have from the past. Anxiety convinces them to play it over and over again, believing that they "could have" done it better or "should have" done something different. Unfortunately, this ends up being a bottomless pit that sucks time and energy away from the person who is aware that nothing can be done about the past and yet they ruminate anyway.

There are also legitimate problems that people worry about. Anxiety can take over when people believe they should have some control over these real problems. The more helpless a person feels, the more fear and worry take over.

*The jump is
so frightening
between where
I am and where
I want to be...
because of all
I may become
I will close my
eyes and leap!*
–Mary Anne
Radmacher

How Do I Get Better?

*Courage is not the absence of fear, but doing
something in spite of fear.*
–Anonymous, *Top 100 Inspirational Quotes for Living Anxiety-Free*

Anxiety Disorders are treatable!

There are three categories of treatment we use which include:
* Medication
* Cognitive-Behavioral Therapy (CBT)
* Complementary Treatments

Many people first seek help from their family doctor or sometimes go to an emergency room during a panic attack. Doctors will often start a person with anxiety on medications called Selective Serotonin Reuptake Inhibitors (SSRI). These medications block the reuptake process in the neurons and, over time, balance serotonin. Serotonin is responsible for your mood, appetite, sleep, and sex drive. This is why you may feel one or all of these areas are affected when you have an anxiety disorder.

Often SSRIs are the first line of treatment, but research shows that cognitive-behavioral therapy is equally or more effective as a first line of treatment and more effective for people who are medication sensitive or for people who do not respond to the medication.* The reason cognitive-behavioral therapy is so effective is that people learn to apply skills, over time, that change their brain. CBT is a systematic treatment approach, targeting distressing thoughts and feelings, that increases coping skills, and decreases avoidance behavior.

Complementary treatment includes approaches that will help you live a more balanced life that is centered in the present. The following pages are a summary of cognitive-behavioral and complementary skills that will help to take the power away from anxiety and give it back to you so you can begin "Living Well with Anxiety."

The mistake people make is having a constant conversation in their head with anxiety rather than doing the things that will make them better. My challenge to you is to choose one skill and do it, every day, until it becomes a habit. Then do one more. Do not think about it, just do it!

*Heldt E, Gus Manfro G, Kipper L, Blaya C, Isolan L, Otto MW; *One-year follow-up of pharmacotherapy-resistant patients with panic disorder treated with cognitive-behavior therapy: Outcome and predictors of remission;* Behav Res Ther. 2006 May;44(5):657-65. Epub 2005 Jul 20.

When I don't do my exposure therapy because I am afraid, this gives OCD power over me as, at that moment, I am saying to OCD, "I can't do this because I believe what you (OCD) are saying is true."

–Debbie, a client

I believe that anyone can conquer fear by doing the things he fears to do, provided he keeps doing them until he gets a record of successful experiences behind him.
–Eleanor Roosevelt

12

Step #1: Bring It On

The only way to get anxiety on the run is to engage it. Look for opportunities to be triggered. Be proactive, not reactive. Most people try to handle the anxiety after they have already been triggered. It's easier to tolerate anxiety when you are purposeful about feeling it. Once you've engaged it, try to make it worse. It's difficult for your brain to see you as vulnerable if you are seeking out opportunities to feel anxious. Choosing to live a life with risks is better than living a life of isolation. It's time to be in the driver's seat and get anxiety on the run!

Linda came to therapy because she was no longer participating in social events due to her fear that she would make a fool of herself. Although she had been able to participate in social events in the past, she never felt completely comfortable and often found herself in a corner waiting for the event to be over. In the past year she decided to decline invitations. She now knows that this only served to give power to her fear and finds herself having anxiety about going anywhere including to the grocery store and work. Through exposure therapy, Linda learned how to purposefully seek out opportunities to feel anxiety in social situations. Rather than avoiding people, she engaged them in small talk, and even began hosting small dinner parties. Although her anxiety still gets triggered, she is able to use all of these skills to quiet it down and enjoy herself. Her motto now is "bring it on!"

I travel precisely because it makes me anxious. I know that if I let anxiety keep me from traveling I could spend the rest of my life sitting in my living room, so I do it because I know I'm going to be nervous and I'm really going to miss my family, but I also know I'll live through it and be happier for having succeeded.
–Eric, a family member of a client

You are the lock, and you are the key.
–Anonymous

Step #2: Do the Opposite

Our instinct is to stay away from pain, so we resist anxiety by avoiding triggers, seeking reassurance, and engaging in compulsions/ behaviors that decrease it.

Daniel came to me after a terrifying flight that left him unable to travel, and then anxiety quickly took over his life by preventing him from going to high places. This took away the things he enjoyed most including climbing, sailing, and traveling. Daniel's anxiety told him to protect himself from these dangerous situations so our therapy was to do the opposite. We started by imagining going to high places, writing stories about these adventures, and eventually climbing to the top of an observation deck that overlooked a lake. Not only was it important for Daniel to do the opposite but he also had to think the opposite. Daniel would tell himself that he would "be fine," "nothing bad would happen during these exposures," but his anxiety levels remained at a high level. So he had to engage in the opposite thoughts to convince anxiety that he was not vulnerable— he could tolerate something bad happening on these adventures.

We can't solve problems by using the same kind of thinking we use when we create them.

–Albert Einstein

As he climbed higher or looked over the observation deck, he had to say to himself, "I might fall and die. I choose to take these risks to live a full life rather than have fear tell me how to live!"

To outsmart anxiety:
- Do the opposite of what fear tells you.
- Move closer to your triggers.
- Take risks.
- Be imperfect by giving 80% instead of 100%.
- Get dirty – find out what really happens when you do what fear tells you not to.
- Remember: Fear is a big bully. When you look it straight in the eye, it will wither away. This is not easy because it goes against everything you believe is keeping you safe, but it is essential to taking back your life.

Anxiety is like a bully - it feels terrifying and wants you to shrink back from it but, once confronted (through doing exposures), it begins to get smaller and lose its ability to make you afraid.
—Debbie S., a client

Step #3: Cognitive Therapy
Why Positive Thoughts Don t Work

People with anxiety engage in extreme thinking that maintains their fear. They get caught up in catastrophic thinking in order to prepare themselves for the worst. This only serves to add fuel to the fire. They may also try to cope with anxiety by taking the other extreme. They will try to think positive thoughts by telling themselves that they will be fine, nothing bad will happen, the chances are slim that anything bad will happen, or everybody else does this so why can't I? Positive thoughts don't work because anxiety will argue with you by saying "what if this time you are not fine, or this might be the one time that something bad does happen." You will never win if you argue with anxiety. Fear will always find a way to mess with you on either extreme, whether you are catastrophizing or trying to be positive.

The key is to stay neutral. Validate your fear and feelings and stick to the facts. "This makes me feel anxious. Even though I feel uncomfortable, I wonder if I can continue. These feelings are just chemicals. Although they are uncomfortable they are not dangerous.

We are both burdened and blessed by the great responsibility of the will - the power of choice. Our future is determined, in large part, by the choices we make now. We cannot always control our circumstances, but we can and do choose our response to whatever arises. Reclaiming the power of choice, we find the courage to live fully in the world.

–Dan Millman, *Top 100 Inspirational Quotes for Living Anxiety-Free*

20

I know anxiety lies to me. It's up to me to decide whether I am going to believe the lie."

Kelly has contamination OCD. It tells her that germs have splashed on her and that she has to avoid anything that has the potential to contaminate her. Before therapy, she believed these lies OCD was telling her. Now she practices being neutral by saying, "I feel contaminated. That usually means it's OCD trying to bully me. I don't know the truth and I will have to live with that doubt. I also choose to live with this uncomfortable feeling without washing or avoiding."

We believe "our lies to be our truths" and we cannot trust our minds to tell us the truth. For the rest of my life I cannot trust my own mind to tell me the truth. That is one thing I have learned in therapy for Body Dysmorphic Disorder.

–Andrea, a client

Step #4: The Role of Family
Making Them Part of the Solution

Having a support system that knows how to validate your feelings without making you feel better is extremely helpful. A good coach will learn how to be present with you while you are struggling and still be able to talk you into facing the fear. They will see you to the other side by challenging you and allowing you to feel the anxiety while celebrating your successes.

There are six steps to coaching that are extremely helpful to someone suffering anxiety:

1. Do not reassure someone who is anxious. Validate their uncomfortable feelings and help them to tolerate these feelings without solving the problem.
2. Be a cheerleader convince them that they can tolerate the anxiety without doing anything to feel better. The anxiety will eventually decrease—sometimes in as little as 15 minutes! Celebrate their ability to stick with the uncomfortable feelings.

3. Challenge them to feel worse. It's the best way to take control of fear. If they can look at a spider, can they touch the spider?
4. Help them change the emotion. Fear gains power through your response. Being upset, crying, getting irritable or downright angry gives anxiety something to feed on. Make a game out of the exposures, get into a competition with the person with anxiety, create a song about the fears, help them get feisty. Anxiety withers away when people are laughing and confident with their exposures.
5. Ask them to rate their anxiety level from 1-10 (10 is a panic attack and 1 is a breeze). This will help you coach them by watching their anxiety level come down over time and by challenging them to increase their anxiety level when they are having success with their exposures.
6. Reward their hard work. This can be a lot of fun. Children love small gifts from the dollar store and adults have all kinds of creative ways to be rewarded!

A coach might say, "I can tell you are really feeling anxious; I wonder if you can feel anxious and drive to the store. You are doing a great job of feeling bad and driving anyway. I wonder if we could take the highway next time and give anxiety a run for its money!

What was your anxiety level when we started to drive? What is it now? I'm really proud of you for driving even though you were at a nine! Let's stop for ice cream to celebrate your hard work."

Having a support system that doesn't give in to anxiety is a crucial part of recovery.

Coaching is as challenging as it is rewarding. My best advice is to clear your mind of everything you have been saying and doing for your family member. For me, I needed to change how I spoke and what I said. It was not easy—I wanted to comfort him and make everything better. Not really a reality. Learning more about PTSD and understanding what was going on in his head and then learning how to coach him when things got "crazy" actually helped us both. Do not be afraid to get support for yourself—it really does help keep things in perspective.
–Gayle, the wife of a client

The only power OCD really has over me is what I give it by believing in its lies.
–Debbie S., a client

Step #5: Safety Behaviors
Why They Don t Keep You Safe

Many people with anxiety engage in behaviors to protect themselves from their perceived danger. Sue always carries her cell phone in the car in case she has a panic attack. Bill has hand sanitizer in case he gets contaminated. Veronica keeps makeup in her briefcase to apply before presentations to hide the blotches that appear on her face. Emily calls her mom several times a day for reassurance when her anxiety is high. These are what we call safety behaviors and although anxiety convinces you they will protect you, they actually don't. Anything that you do that helps you to feel better about your fear only gives information to your brain that the situation must be dangerous or you wouldn't have to be protecting yourself. It becomes a self-fulfilling prophecy: the more you protect yourself, the worse your anxiety becomes. So when you practice doing things that trigger your fears, be sure to leave your protection behind so that your brain will learn the difference between danger and discomfort.

Eileen developed panic attacks. By the time she came to therapy she was only driving within a mile of her house or she had to be within a mile of a hospital in case she had an attack, which she was always tricked into believing would be a heart attack that could kill her. She also had to have her cell phone with her and had to be talking to her husband or her mother while she was driving (she realized the absurdity of this!). Her therapy involved increasing the distance that she drove without any safety behaviors. First she drove around the block with her cell phone but without talking. Then she drove that block with the cell phone but turned it off. Then she left her cell phone at home and eventually increased her distance from home and hospitals. Now she is driving across town, to the mall, and to visit family and friends. She is always proactive and leaves her protection at home.

Stand up to the obstacles and do something about them. You will find that they haven't half the strength you think they have.
–Norman Vincent Peale

Most fears are just illusions.
–Gary Null, *Top 100 Inspirational Quotes for Living Anxiety-Free*

Experiencing social anxiety is like living with blinders on.
Treatment is about expanding your tunnel vision to see a more
complete picture of the world.
—Megan, a client

Step #6: Breathe

People with anxiety tend to take shallow breaths, using only the top half of their diaphragm. This creates an imbalance of oxygen and carbon dioxide which sends a message to their brain that they really are in danger, so their brain sends more anxiety chemicals to prepare them to flee from the danger. This process is often instinctual, so it's important to learn how to be purposeful about your breath to disarm this response.

Your breath is the most powerful tool you have. It's free and always available. Although it is an unconscious process, we can also make it conscious. Start with an exhale, bringing your belly in as you release all of the air. Now inhale, bringing the air all the way down to your tummy, blowing it up like a balloon. Continue to breathe like this, making the exhale longer than the inhale. Having a longer exhale will engage the relaxation response and will trigger your brain to realize you are not in danger. Just 5 breaths/minute will help center you and quiet your anxiety.

> *Sometimes the most important thing in a whole day is the rest we take between two deep breaths.*
> –Etty Hillesum

*When I dance,
I dance; when
I sleep, I sleep;
yes, and when I
walk alone in a
beautiful orchard,
if my thoughts
drift to far-off
matters for some
part of the time
for some other
part, I lead them
back again to the
walk, the orchard,
to the sweetness
of this solitude,
to myself.*
–Montaigne

Step #7: Be Mindful

Mindfulness is a powerful way to live with any type of suffering. Anxiety prefers that you live in the past or worry about the future. Mindfulness gives you the ability to be in the present.

The key components include: Being present with your experience; allowing the experience to be what it is (we are not trying to change it); accepting your experience without judgment (they are not good or bad, they are just feelings and thoughts are just air).

There are several ways to practice mindfulness. Some helpful ways to use mindfulness for anxiety include:

1. *Labeling*—When you are experiencing a worry or an obsession, label it by saying, "just a thought." This helps take the power away from the fear and helps you not engage the thought.

2. *Use your senses*—When you are overwhelmed with anxious feelings or thoughts, you can center yourself by paying attention to what you can see, hear, feel, or taste. You cannot pay attention to anxiety when you are paying attention to your senses.

3. *Acceptance vs. resistance*—The more you learn to accept your anxious feelings, the less power they have over you. Most people

want to get away from anxiety, but the key is to allow it to be and it will grow quieter. If you resist it, it will gain power.

4. *Note the details of what you see*—"There's a tree, there's a road with gravel on it, there's a yellow flower," etc. This helps take you out of the anxiety loop and back into the present moment.

5. *Just the facts*—People with anxiety tend to see things in an exaggerated way, making a stressful situation seem overwhelming. With this technique, you stick just to the facts by telling yourself only the truths about the situation, leaving out anything that is left to judgment or interpretation.

My OCD has a strong and insatiable appetite for isolation and guilt, it chokes on the reality that I am never alone and that 'I am' and have always been enough.
–Andrea, a client

I can survive the anxious feelings that accompany OCD. In fact, I have to allow those feelings to come, feel them, and remember they will pass. Feelings are a part of life. They are not good or bad. They are all "okay."
–Debbie S., a client

When my anxiety is triggered and I begin to feel like my thoughts/ feelings are BIG (catastrophic), I tend to use the "Just" Statements. For me, it is a quick, simple and effective tool. I simply say to myself such things as: "JUST anxiety," "JUST nervous," JUST worrying," JUST scared," etc. In doing this, it seems to minimize the thought/ feeling...as though I am putting a "period" on that particular thought/feeling. It also helps me to ACCEPT the thought/feeling which gives me the chance to think more clearly. If needed, I can then begin another tool to bring my anxiety/nervousness/worrying to an even lower level. You can also use the "JUST" statements for other thoughts/feelings, such as: "Just Sad," or "Just Angry," etc.
–Debbie L., a client

The Emotional Freedom Technique (EFT) is a very quick way to create some distance from anxiety so that you can continue with the skills that are helpful.

Step #8: Tap It Out

Emotional Freedom Technique (EFT) combines tapping on acupuncture points while focusing on the fear and the feelings that fear creates. Energy psychologists believe that anxiety results from a block in your "chi" which is your energy, often creating an emotional imbalance. Once the block is removed, the energy can flow freely. EFT is an approach that draws its power from Eastern discoveries that have been around for over 5,000 years. We know that everything is composed of energy (including our bodies). Although Western Medicine has largely ignored the mind-body-spirit connection, more recently physicians are reconsidering the importance of these connections and the truth that everything is energy, which is allowing us to explore the potential that this knowledge offers us.

An EFT treatment involves the use of fingertips to tap on the end points of various nerves that are situated just beneath the surface of the skin. This unusual but scientific routine decreases arousal in your brain as you are tapping on the fear/feeling and allows energy to flow freely. The "charge" and resulting anxiety related to the emotionally disturbing circumstance are then removed. This treatment is noninvasive and allows the change to be simple and as pain free as possible.

This is a very quick way to create some distance from anxiety so that you can continue with the skills that are helpful. For panic sufferers, once you have learned the EFT process, you can apply it at the onset of an attack and, in many cases, it will quiet the panic within minutes. Not only can there be short-term relief, but people also find that EFT can quiet their anxiety long-term as well. EFT can be accomplished in one or several rounds. However, some anxiety has deeper causes and may need an experienced therapist to help release these. This is very easy to learn by having a practitioner teach you or by going to a website like www.eftuniverse.com.

> *Getting shots at the doctor's office is scary. Doing taps before I get a shot helps to make me feel less scared.*
> –Nicole, an eleven year old client

You have a choice on how anxiety changes your life; you can let it bring you down or you can let it be a motivation for you to go to places you never thought possible!"
–Derick, client (photo of Derick in competition after using EFT)

Today I am off meds and lost all the weight from depression and medications for depression. My story on Tapping begins with sitting in a doctor's office waiting room (My PTSD is connected to Doctors and Nurses.) to do my exposure work with my therapist. It was a living hell to sit there for ten minutes. I sat next to the door of the bathroom and when asked why, I replied, "if a nurse came into the room I could escape into the bathroom before she could get me." When I decided that I could do no more exposure work, my therapist asked me to try a new therapy called Tapping (EFT). Not long after "tapping," we visited a doctor's waiting room, the hall and treatment rooms. I looked at things on the counter. Did I say we walked past the nurse and spoke to her?! Only 20 years between being in a doctor's office and going back.

–Jeff, a client

The difference between try and triumph is a little "umph."

—Anonymous, *Top 100 Inspirational Quotes for Living Anxiety-Free*

Step #9: Exercise

Exercise is non-negotiable. It is the only thing, other than medication, that will help balance serotonin, the chemical that is responsible for those yucky feelings. Start small. If you can't run, can you walk? If you don't have 30 minutes to exercise, do you have 10 minutes? Yoga is a wonderful combination of breathing, cardiovascular, stretching, balance and meditation. Start with one class a week and you will see a difference!

It isn't the act of exercising that is tough for me. It is taking the first step and actually doing it. Once I do though, I have an energy shift that makes me feel better and think more clearly!
–Michelle, a client

44

Step #10: Become Balanced

Anxiety loves a person who is not balanced, and anxious people tend to be very busy because they find the more distracted they are the less their anxious thoughts bother them. However this is a treadmill that no one wants to be on, because the busier you are, the more stressed you become, and the more anxiety will creep in. Remember, whatever you do to keep the anxiety at bay, the more likely it is to return. Ultimately, one has to work towards having a balance in caring for yourself, your family, and work obligations. It's crucial to put yourself first by taking time in your day to exercise, be mindful, or meditate. Create spaces that allow you to breathe. As you regain balance, you will not be as vulnerable, and anxiety will have less to mess with.

You will never change your life until you change something you do daily!
–Anonymous, *Top 100 Inspirational Quotes for Living Anxiety-Free*

Sometimes the paths we take are long and hard, but remember:
those are the ones that lead to the most beautiful views.
–Anonymous, *Top 100 Inspirational Quotes for Living Anxiety-Free*

Final Thoughts

We are all experts on anxiety. We know the awful feeling that eats away at our gut. We are aware of how anxiety makes us more irritable with our family members. We are certain that there are so many ways anxiety has made our life smaller because of avoidance. This book was written to show you how you can also know peace, have hope, take risks, and be in healthy relationships. I love my job! I get the opportunity to watch people transform from living in isolation with anxiety to living free with their authentic selves. Part of your journey will be to rediscover who you truly are without anxiety bullying you.

It is not easy to put these simple skills to use on a daily basis. Anxiety will give you a thousand excuses not to practice these skills. It will be difficult to face your fears, knowing the suffering you will have to endure. However, that suffering is only temporary and you can do anything that is temporary. Most of my clients tell me the hardest part of this treatment is making the decision to do it. Once they begin with one small thing, they often find that anxiety withers away and was not the monster they believed it to be. Go ahead, take one small step to taking your life back and join all of us who have learned to live well with anxiety!

Through these techniques I went from 17 pills a day to one antidepressant. I took a trip across the country before our children were born. And I was inspired to go on to graduate school to get my master's in counseling. Anxiety continues to rear its ugly head in my life from time to time and in those moments I do not let it trap me as I once did. I understand it.

I continue to live my life through it. I do everything that my anxiety would once have me afraid of doing- even in full panic. Because now I know that I am stronger than my anxiety. There is a way out. I was in the darkest place. Looking back sometimes I don't know how I even survived. But if there is anything I can tell others who struggle like I did, it is this: I promise you, there is a way out. It will not always be this awful.

–Ellen, a client

Resources

These are some of the resources that I have found to be helpful for my clients:

Anxiety –General:
- *Feel The Fear and Do It Anyway* by Susan Jeffers, Ph.D.
- *The Anxiety and Phobia Workbook* by Edmund J. Bourne
- *Calming Your Anxious Mind* by Jeffrey Brantley and Jon Kabat-Zinn (mindfulness and anxiety)
- *Freeing Your Child From Anxiety* by Tamar E. Chansky, Ph.D.

Panic:
- *Don't Panic* by Reid Wilson
- *Facing Panic: Self Help for People with Panic Attacks* by Reid Wilson
- *Anxiety, Phobias, and Panic* by Reneau Peurifoy, M.A.

Obsessive Compulsive Disorder:
- *Up and Down The Worry Hill* by Aureen Pinto Wagner, Ph.D. (for children)
- *Getting Control* by Lee Baer, Ph.D.
- *Brain Lock* by Jeffrey Schwartz, Ph.D.
- *Obsessive Compulsive Disorder: New Help for the Family* by Herbert Gravitz, Ph.D.
- *The Imp Of The Mind* by Lee Baer, Ph.D.(about violent and sexual thoughts)
- *The Doubting Disease* by Joseph Ciarrocchi (scrupulosity and religious obsessions)
- *Tormenting Thoughts And Secret Rituals* by Ian Osborn, M.D.

- *Managing Obsessive-Compulsive Disorder: A Sufferer's Question and Answer Guide* by Mark Berger, Ph.D. (must email author for book)
- *Overcoming Compulsive Hoarding* by Patricia Perkins

Body Dysmorphic Disorder:

- *The BDD Workbook* by James Claiborn, Ph.D. and Cherry Pedrick, R.N.
- *The Broken Mirror* by Katherine Phillips, M.D.

Online Resources:

- Obsessive Compulsive Foundation (www.iocdf.org)
- Anxiety Disorders Association of America (www.adaa.org)
- Trichotillomania Learning Center (www.trich.org)
- Amy Weintraub (www.yogafordepression.com)
- Emotional Freedom Techniques (www.eftuniverse.com)
- Affirmations (www.louisehay.com)
- Anxiety Coaching (www.anxietycoach.com)
- Resource for Audio CD's for Meditation (www.healthjourneys.com)

Audio CDs:

- *Let My Words Be Your Words* by Francoise Adan

You have within you right now, everything you need to deal with whatever the world can throw at you.
–Brian Tracy, *Top 100 Inspirational Quotes for Living Anxiety-Free*

Invite Kimberly to speak at your upcoming event!

WORKSHOPS

Kimberly is available to present workshop and trainings for:

- *Colleges/Universities*
- *Schools (Teacher/Parent Presentations)*
- *Wellness Events*
- *Conferences*
- *Women's Groups*
- *Churches*
- *Organizations (Management/Employee presentations)*

To see Kimberly's schedule of events and workshop topics or to book Kimberly for your upcoming event, please visit:

www.livingwellwithanxiety.com

Kimberly has years of experience, as well as wisdom and wit acquired from treating thousands of individuals and families who suffer from anxiety... She is a sought after speaker, trainer and clinician who offers the best that science has to offer in understanding and overcoming anxiety.
–Karen Cassiday, Star of Animal Planet's *Confessions: Animal Hoarder*

It has been a while since I attended a workshop that offered so many treatment strategies in such a succinct, down-to-earth, client-friendly, and efficient manner. Kimberly has a special gift of delivery of the material that she has so obviously mastered in her practice over the years. I have been sharing the workshop "gems" with my colleagues and we look forward to incorporating them into our therapy sessions. She has brought new life to our work!
–Sue Daley, M.A., a counselor at Penn State Behrend

How can Kimberly's presentations benefit you?

Kimberly works with individuals, families, mental health professionals, educators and anyone interested in learning how to gain control over anxiety symptoms and how to live a more balanced, peaceful life.

Kimberly is an expert in the field of anxiety. She is a dynamic speaker who engages her audiences, providing knowledge in the most up-to-date, empirically-based techniques for managing anxiety and stress.

In her workshops, Kimberly provides an energy-filled day with many opportunities to practice skills that will help individuals control anxiety levels, create quiet space in the midst of chaos and gain distance from their emotions so they can develop healthier patterns in their work and family.

Kimberly's workshops allow staff to become more productive and creative when anxiety and fear are no longer draining their energy and affecting their decision-making.

WORKSHOPS

KIMBERLY J♨Y MORROW
WORKSHOPS

Living Well Series—This experiential workshop series teaches five key skills to create balance and allows participants to practice these skills to have optimal functioning in their home and work environments.

Face It and Feel It—A workshop that teaches individuals how to live fully with anxiety by exposing them to their fears and helping them to learn specific skills so that anxiety no longer has power over them.

Complementary Approaches to Treating Anxiety and Depression—A workshop designed for mental health professionals to learn ways to take care of themselves and their clients by teaching: Mindfulness, Meditation, Breathing, Affirmation, and the Emotional Freedom Technique.

Embracing Discomfort: Learning How To Do Exposure and Response Prevention with Anxiety Disorders—A workshop for mental health professionals to teach them the art of exposure and response prevention.

Anxiety Tools for Kids—A workshop for kids or for professionals that work with kids. It is a kid-friendly approach to exposure and response prevention.

Coaching: How to Help Your Friend or Family Member with Anxiety—A workshop to teach friends, families and professionals how to talk someone through anxiety. Offers important skills to empower the one you love rather than empower anxiety.

Anxiety Disorder Workshop—A seminar on treatment strategies for Panic, OCD, and Trichotillomania.

Anxiety Skills for Children—A curriculum to teach school children about anxiety.

Anxiety and Social Skills for School Age Children—Educate School District counselors, mental health professionals, and behavioral specialists on how to help children who are experiencing anxiety and social skills deficits in school.

"Face It and Feel It"

www.livingwellwithanxiety.com